The CHARACTERS

Tear out this page.
Punch out Jenny, Baxter,
Ned, Ivy, and Robert.
Throw the scraps away.
Read the story.
Then act it out.
Make up other stories
of your own.

Jenny

B

Baxter

J

Ned

N

Mr. Moose
is on page 24.

I

Ivy

R

Robert

Late for the Bus

It was raining when the school bus arrived.

Everyone climbed aboard in raincoats.

"Baxter's missing," said Mr. Moose, the driver.

He looked out the window

and saw something yellow coming closer and closer.

It was Baxter Bear, running like crazy.

"Wait for me!" yelled Baxter.

"Slow down!" shouted Mr. Moose.

But Baxter didn't slow down.

He ran into the bus full speed and tripped.

His lunch box went flying,

and everybody laughed.

Slowly Baxter picked himself up.

"What a rotten day," he said.

"It must be the rain."

A

N   R   B   I

R   N   I

Chapter 2

The Talent Show Box

In school everyone sat down.

Mr. Moose, who was the teacher too,

put names on the job chart.

He put IVY next to FEED FISH.

He put NED next to FEED TURTLE.

He put JENNY next to WEATHER PICTURE.

He put ROBERT next to PUT AWAY BOOKS.

Baxter got DUSTING.

"What a bad day," he said.

"First I was late, then I fell down,

and now I'll get dust in my nose."

When the jobs were done,

Mr. Moose pointed to a box on the desk and said,

"This is a Talent Show Box.

Each of you will pull a prop from the box

and use the prop in an act for a show.

Make a costume for your act,

and think of a rhyming poem to say aloud.

We'll put on our show this afternoon

and invite the rest of the school to watch.

There will be prizes at the end

for the best acts.

I'm not going to watch you choose your props

because I want to be surprised."

Mr. Moose left the room.

Jenny reached in the box

and pulled out a gold wand.

Robert pulled out a black cape.

Ned pulled out swim fins.

Ivy pulled out a big red ball.

Baxter shut his eyes

and hoped for something wonderful.

He felt something small and hard.

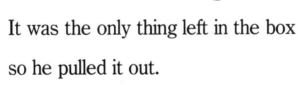

It was the only thing left in the box

so he pulled it out.

"Tape?" he asked. "A roll of black tape?

What am I supposed to do with that?"

Everybody laughed.

Chapter 3

Worried at Lunch

In the cafeteria everyone was talking.

"Trade you an apple for a cupcake," Ned said.

"Okay," said Robert.

"Trade you a tuna for a cheese," said Jenny.

"Deal," said Ivy.

Baxter took out a peanut butter sandwich,

a can of apple juice, and a peach.

He knew Ned liked peaches,

but he didn't offer to trade.

"If I do, he'll laugh at me," Baxter thought.

"That's the kind of bad day it is."

He could hear the others

talking about their acts.

"I'm going to be Dracula," said Robert.

"What rhymes with neck?"

"I'm going to be a clown," said Ivy.

"What rhymes with ball?"

"Fall," said Baxter, trying to be nice.

"Just like you did this morning!" said Ivy.

Everybody laughed at Baxter again.

Baxter was furious.

He hated to be laughed at.

Most of all he hated his stupid roll of tape.

What kind of a prop was that?

He wished he had something better.

He didn't know what he was going to do.

Mr. Moose came into the cafeteria.

"The sun came out," he said.

"If you like, you can go outside

to work on your poems and costumes."

Everyone but Baxter

grabbed a lunch box and left.

Baxter finished eating slowly.

Then he went outside too.

Chapter 4

Sitting on the Slide

On the picnic table

Robert cut out a black paper bat.

Ned cut out something yellow and something gray.

Baxter sat on top of the slide.

"Guess what I'm going to be?" asked Jenny.

She came over, waving her wand.

"A fairy princess?" asked Baxter.

"No!" she said. "Guess again!"

But Baxter wouldn't guess.

"Go away," he said.

"I can't think with you around."

Jenny ran off and cut out a pink crown.

Baxter felt terrible.

He didn't know what to be.

He couldn't think of anything to cut out.

He couldn't think of a costume.

He couldn't think of a poem.

Worst of all,

a bee was buzzing around his head.

Baxter had to sit real still

so the bee wouldn't sting him.

"Shoo!" he yelled. "I'm trying to think!"

But the bee wouldn't go away.

It kept buzzing and buzzing and buzzing

around Baxter's head.

That made Baxter madder than ever.

"How can I think about this tape

when all I can think of is that bee?"

Suddenly Baxter slid down the slide

and ran into school.

He got out his raincoat and a pair of scissors.

He started cutting up his tape.

Maybe it wasn't such a bad day after all.

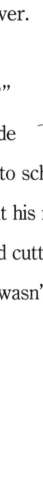

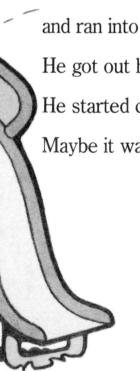

Chapter 5

The Talent Show

In the auditorium all the performers sat on the stage.

Everyone wore a costume except Baxter.

He had his raincoat folded on his lap.

Mr. Moose went up to the mike and said,

"The act that gets the most claps will win."

Ned hopped forward dressed like a frog.

He held up a sun and a cloud and said,

> *One for the money, two for the show,*
> *Rain or shine, watch me go!*

He hopped back and forth

and got enough claps for five bows.

Robert ran to the mike with his paper bat.

> *My bat and I are very mean.*
> *The meanest creatures you've ever seen.*
> *Watch out!*

Robert got enough for three bows.

Ivy came forward dressed as a clown.

> *I'm a clown, here's my ball!*
> *I toss it up, and down I fall!*

She fell down funny like a clown.

Ivy got enough claps for six bows.

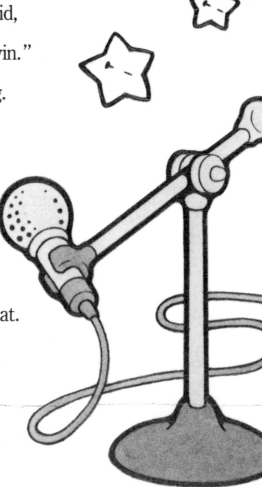

Jenny ran up to the mike and said,

> *I'm not the Queen of England,*
> *I'm not Princess Di,*
> *I reach under your pillow,*
> *Who am I?*

There was a long pause,

and then someone yelled, "The Tooth Fairy!"

Jenny got enough claps for eight bows.

"I'll never beat that," said Baxter.

But he put on his raincoat and began anyway:

> *Hubba hubba ding ding,*
> *I'm a bee and I can sting!*
> *Shooby, dooby, be, bop,*
> *Tape is not an easy prop.*

Everyone laughed and clapped.

Baxter got enough claps for ten bows!

Mr. Moose gave out the prizes.

Ned's prize said LIVELIEST.

Robert's said SCARIEST,

Ivy's said FUNNIEST, and Jenny's said PRETTIEST.

But Baxter's prize said BEST OF ALL.

Mr. Moose told everyone

that the tape had been in the box by mistake.

He said it was absolutely amazing

that Baxter had found a way to use it.

"I guess today's my lucky day," said Baxter.

"It must have been the rain."

The End.

Performer

M

B

J

21

Special Instructions

To put the characters in the school bus, match them with their shadows. Slide them into place from the back.

To have the characters choose their Talent Show Props, slide the props up through the slot in the Talent Show Box. The characters can hold the props in their hands.

The easiest way to set up the props in the cafeteria scene is to put them in the slots in alphabetical order.

To fit the characters in their chairs on the stage, overlap them slightly. Three go in the first row, and two go in the second row.

Mr. Moose's
show clothes

Mr. Moose

24

Slip wings
behind head.

Fold

Hook around
Baxter's head
below his ears.

Fold

B

B

I

s

h

B

z

I

J

r

p

I

25

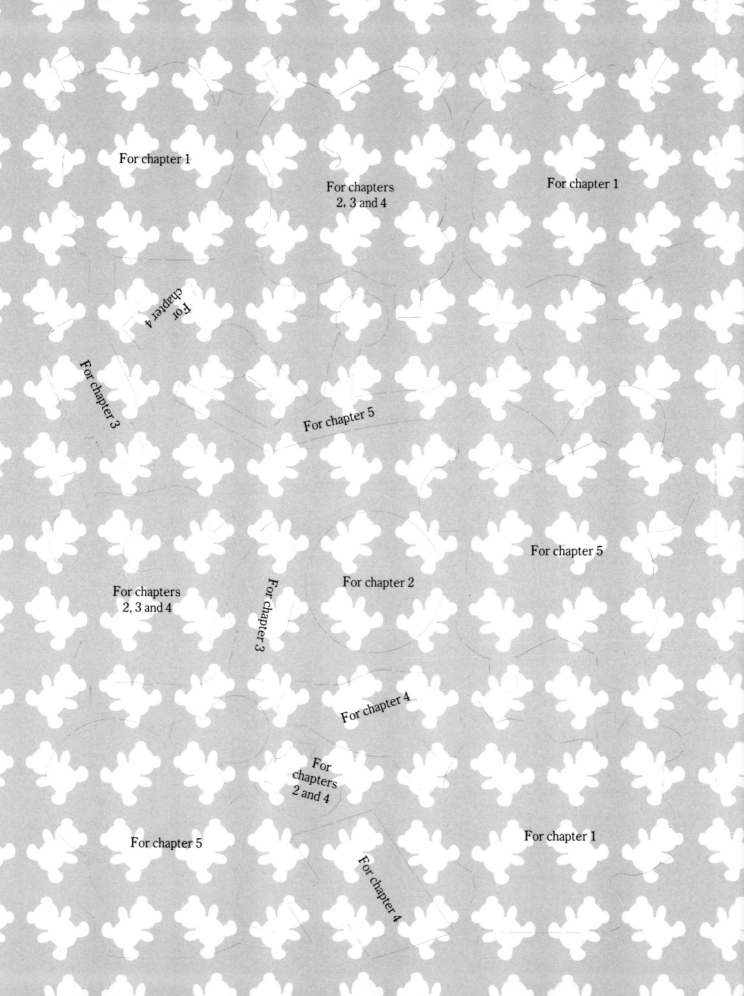

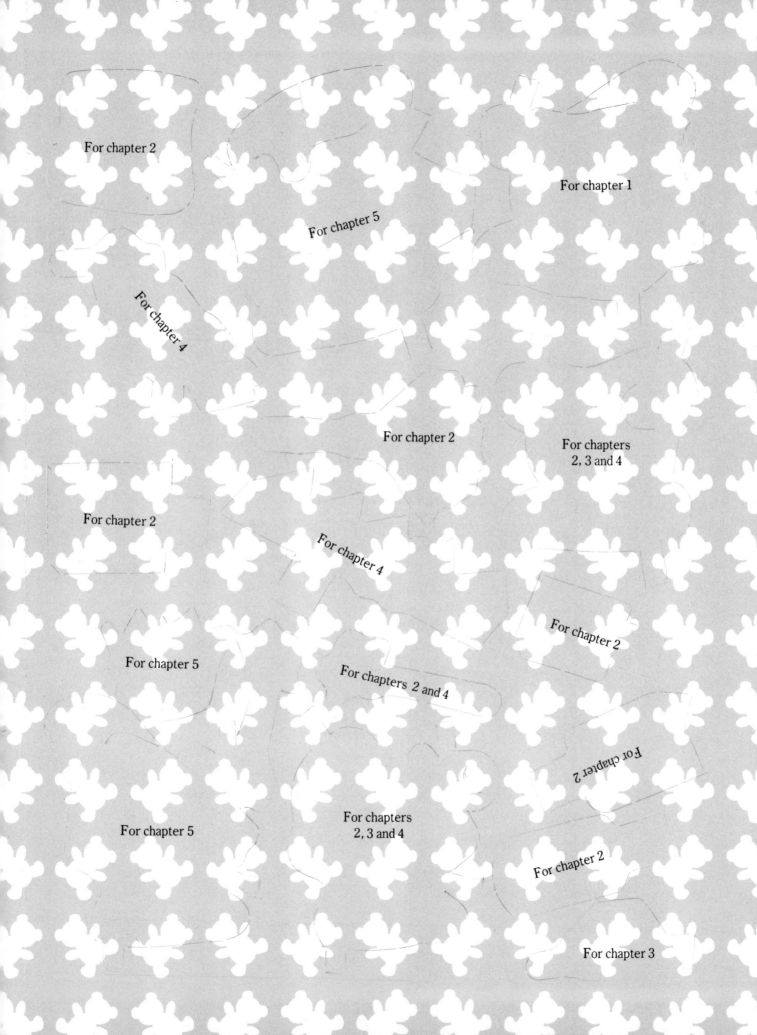

Slip neck in slot.

Slip collar behind head.

Put duster in slot in Baxter's hand.

Set crown in ear slots on Jenny's head.

Put wand in hand slot.

TURTLE FOOD

FISH FOOD

28

Choose the right weather picture.